P9-CDW-553

POEMS YOU'LL LIKE

Potato Chips and a Slice of Moon

Selected by Lee Bennett Hopkins
and Misha Arenstein

Illustrated by Wayne Blickenstaff

SCHOLASTIC INC.
New York Toronto London Auckland Sydney

Cover photo by D. Logan/H. Armstrong Roberts, Inc.

ISBN 0-590-40213-7

Copyright © 1976 by Scholastic Inc. All rights reserved. Published by Scholastic Inc., 730 Broadway, New York, NY 10003.

12 11 10 9 8 7 6 5 4 3 2 1   3   6 7 8 9/8 0 1/9

Printed in the U.S.A.   11

The title of this book is drawn from two poems, "Street Song" and "Abstract Picture: At the Museum" in THE WAY THINGS ARE AND OTHER POEMS by Myra Cohn Livingston, with permission of the author.

For reprint permission grateful acknowledgment is made to:

Steve Allen for "Flight," © 1956 by Steve Allen from WRY ON THE ROCKS.

T. D. Allen for poems from ARROWS FOUR, Prose and Poetry by Young American Indians, edited by T. D. Allen and published by Simon & Schuster, Inc. in 1974: "My Heavy Chevy" by Dallas Belgarde; "Gah'-Chac-Ah" by Cecil E. Johnson, Jr. and "Stream" and "Rain" by Darlene Parisien.

Atheneum Publishers, Inc. for "A dream . . ." by Joan Walsh Anglund from GOODBYE, YESTERDAY: A Book of Poems, © 1974 by Joan Walsh Anglund; "The Porcupine" and "Up State and Down State" (fourth stanza only of "Up and Down") by N. M. Bodecker from LET'S MARRY SAID THE CHERRY (A Margaret K. McElderry Book), © 1974 by N. M. Bodecker; "Marbles" by Kathleen Fraser from STILTS, SOMERSAULTS, AND HEADSTANDS, © 1968 by Kathleen Fraser; "The Black Snake" by Patricia Hubbell from 8 A. M. SHADOWS, © 1965 by Patricia Hubbell; "Growing: For Louis," "Beach," "Street Song," "Abstract Picture: At the Museum" (first and last stanzas only) by Myra Cohn Livingston from THE WAY THINGS ARE AND OTHER POEMS (A Margaret K. McElderry Book), © 1974 by Myra Cohn Livingston; "Associations" and "Mean Song" by Eve Merriam from THERE IS NO RHYME FOR SILVER, © 1962 by Eve Merriam; "Teevee" and "Bam, Bam, Bam" by Eve Merriam from CATCH A LITTLE RHYME, © 1966 by Eve Merriam; "Spectacular" by Lilian Moore from I THOUGHT I HEARD THE CITY, text © 1969 by Lilian Moore; "Squirrel" and "Encounter" by Lilian Moore from SAM'S PLACE, POEMS FROM THE COUNTRY, text © 1973 by Lilian Moore; "Sound of Water" by Mary O'Neill from WHAT IS THAT SOUND? text © 1966 by Mary O'Neill.

Joanna Cole for "Driving to the Beach" by Joanna Cole, © 1973 by Joanna Cole.

Thomas Y. Crowell Company, Inc. for "On Mother's Day" by Aileen Fisher from SKIP AROUND THE YEAR, © 1967 by Aileen Fisher; "Winter" by Aileen Fisher from IN ONE DOOR AND OUT THE OTHER, © 1969 by Aileen Fisher; "Early Spring in the Blackberry Patch" and "Hot Enough to See" by Robert Froman from SEEING THINGS, © 1974 by Robert Froman.

Doubleday & Company, Inc. for "Pony Language" by Kookie Jenkins from WORD MAGIC by Charleen Whisnant and Jo Hassett, © 1974 by Charleen Whisnant and Jo Hassett; and "The cemetery stones . . ." and "When time was a boy . . ." by George Mendoza from THE MIST MEN AND OTHER POEMS, © 1970 by George Mendoza.

E. P. Dutton & Co., Inc. for "A Thought" by Marchette Chute from AROUND AND ABOUT by Marchette Chute, © 1957 by E. P. Dutton & Co., Inc.; first and last verses of "Deserted" by Madison Cawein from THE VALE OF TEMPE, copyright 1905 by Madison Cawein; "Three Skies" by Claudia Lewis from POEMS OF EARTH AND SPACE, © 1967 by Claudia Lewis.

Charles J. Egita for "Passing By the Junkyard" by Charles J. Egita.

Farrar, Straus & Giroux, Inc. for "The Story-Teller" by Mark Van Doren from COLLECTED AND NEW POEMS, 1924–1963, © 1963 by Mark Van Doren.

Follett Publishing Company for "The Flying Squirrel" and "Noses" from THE DAY IS DANCING by Rowena Bennett. Copyright © 1948, 1968 by Rowena Bennett.

Garrard Publishing Co. for "Eight Witches" by B. J. Lee from ARITHMETIC IN VERSE AND RHYME, selected by Allan D. Jacobs and Leland B. Jacobs, © 1971 by Garrard Publishing Co.

John Goldthwaite for "Superzero" and "Coney Island", © 1976 by John Goldthwaite.

Ruth Belov Gross for "Some lollipops last a long, long time . . ." from THE LAUGH BOOK, text © 1971 by Ruth Belov Gross.

Grosset & Dunlap, Inc. for "I Was So Lonesome" by Joan Berg Victor from DO YOU REALLY LOVE ME? © 1973 by Joan Berg Victor.

Harcourt Brace Jovanovich, Inc. for "Tomato Time" from THE MOON AND A STAR, AND OTHER POEMS, © 1965 by Myra Cohn Livingston; "Soup" from SMOKE AND STEEL by Carl Sandburg, copyright 1920 by Harcourt Brace Jovanovich, Inc.; renewed 1948 by Carl Sandburg; "You Can Go Now" from THE PEOPLE, YES by Carl Sandburg, copyright 1936 by Harcourt Brace Jovanovich, Inc., renewed 1964 by Carl Sandburg.

Margaret Hillert for "Walking In The Fog," "About Feet," "Enchanted Sky," and "Tracks In The Snow" by Margaret Hillert from FARTHER THAN FAR, © 1969 by Margaret Hillert.

Holt, Rinehart and Winston, Publishers for "The Runaway" and "The Secret Sits" by Robert Frost from THE POETRY OF ROBERT FROST edited by Edward Connery Lathem. Copyright 1923, © 1969 by Holt, Rinehart and Winston. Copyright 1942, 1951 by Robert Frost. Copyright © 1970 by Lesley Frost Ballantine; 4 lines from "Puppy" by Lee Bennett Hopkins from KIM'S PLACE, © 1974 by Lee Bennett Hopkins; "K" by Leland B. Jacobs from ALPHABET OF GIRLS, © 1969 by Leland B. Jacobs.

Houghton Mifflin Company for nine lines from "Sky Diver" by Adrien Stoutenberg from SHORT HISTORY OF THE FUR TRADE, © 1968 by Adrien Stoutenberg; and "Wind and Silver" by Amy Lowell from THE COMPLETE WORKS OF AMY LOWELL.

The Instructor Publications, Inc. for "A Football Game" by Alice Van Eck from INSTRUCTOR, © 1960 by The Instructor Publications, Inc.

Bobbi Katz for "Hi-Rise," "Winter Remedy," and "If I Could Be an Astronaut" by Bobbi Katz, © 1976 by Bobbi Katz.

Alfred A. Knopf, Inc. for "All These I Hear" from WHISPERINGS AND OTHER THINGS by Dahlov Ipcar, © 1967 by Dahlov Ipcar; "One Day" by Wilford Horne, Jr., "When the plants begin to grow" by Vanessa Fraser, "Thunder" by Philip Arenstein, "Ice Cream" by Lynn Mead from CITY TALK, compiled by Lee Bennett Hopkins, © 1970 by Lee Bennett Hopkins.

Lerner Publications Company for "Skating" from SWING AROUND THE SUN by Barbara Juster Esbensen, © 1965 by Lerner Publications Company.

Little, Brown and Company for "The Kitten," "Arthur," and "Edouard," Copyright 1940 by Ogden Nash; "The Termite," Copyright 1942 by Ogden Nash from VERSES FROM 1929 ON by Ogden Nash; "The Lamb," © 1955 by Ogden Nash (This poem originally appeared in *The Saturday Evening Post*) from THE FACE IS FAMILIAR by Ogden Nash; "An Introduction to Dogs," Copyright 1938 by Ogden Nash from FAMILY REUNION by Ogden Nash.

Macmillan Publishing Co., Inc. for "What Is Once Loved" by Elizabeth Coatsworth from ALICE ALL BY HERSELF, copyright 1937 by Macmillan Publishing Co., Inc., renewed 1965 by Elizabeth Coatsworth Beston.

Michael B. Mager for "Mistake" by Michael B. Mager, © 1976 by Michael B. Mager.

Lillian Morrison for "Kickoff" from SPRINTS AND DISTANCES, © 1965 by Lillian Morrison. Published by Thomas Y. Crowell Company, Inc.

William Morrow & Co., Inc. for "Stickball" by Virginia Schonborg from SUBWAY SWINGER, © 1970 by Virginia Schonborg.

Harold Ober Associates Incorporated for "Trip: San Francisco" by Langston Hughes from THE LANGSTON HUGHES READER, © 1958 by Langston Hughes.

Random House, Inc. for "The 1st" by Lucille Clifton from GOOD TIMES, © 1969 by Lucille Clifton.

Paul R. Reynolds, Inc. for "Old Jake Sutter" by Kaye Starbird from DON'T EVER CROSS A CROCODILE, © 1963 by Kaye Starbird.

Marci Ridlon Carafoli for "Catching Quiet" and "Faces" by Marci Ridlon.

Louis B. Salomon for first five lines of "Univac to Univac" by Louis B. Salomon from SOME HAYSTACKS DON'T EVEN HAVE ANY NEEDLE, © 1958 by Harper's Magazine, Inc.

Charles Scribner's Sons for "The Ant Village" by Marion Edey and Dorothy Grider from OPEN THE DOOR, copyright 1949 by Marion Edey and Dorothy Grider; "City Street" and "Coca Cola Sunset" by Felice Holman from I HEAR YOU SMILING, © 1973 by Felice Holman; "If ever you . . ." by Arnold Spilka from AND THE FROG WENT "BLAH!" © 1972 by Arnold Spilka.

Simon & Schuster, Inc. for "Lying in the sun . . ." by Ian Johnson and "A leaf . . ." by Jennifer Hodgman from MIRACLES by Richard Lewis, © 1966 by Richard Lewis.

The Society of Authors and Miss Pamela Hinkson for "August Weather" by Katharine Tynan.

Debra Thurr for "Day Moon" by Debra Thurr, © 1976 by Debra Thurr.

The Viking Press, Inc. for "A Mountain View" by Rose Burgunder from SUMMER TO SUMMER, © 1965 by Rose Styron.

Frederick Warne & Co., Inc. for "Owls Aren't So Smart" by Richard Shaw from THE OWL BOOK, © 1970 by Frederick Warne & Co., Inc.

Franklin Watts, Inc. for "How I Got To Be a Princess" by Bobbi Katz from UPSIDE DOWN AND INSIDE OUT: Poems for All Your Pockets, © 1973 by Bobbi Katz.

Estate of Miss E. Wolfe for lines from "Autumn" by Humbert Wolfe from HUMORESQUE in FOUR SEASONS, FIVE SENSES, selected by Elinor Parker.

Xerox Education Publications for "Cinquain" by Therese LaBlanc, "The First Christmas" by Rhonda Whewell, "Haiku" by Kevin Maas, and "Snowflakes" by Debbie Hastings from Read Magazine, © 1974 by Xerox Corp.

POTATO CHIPS

O, I have been walking
with a bag of potato chips,
me and potato chips
munching along,

Walking alone
eating potato chips,
big old potato chips,
crunching along,

walking along
munching potato chips,
me and potato chips
lunching along.

Street Song
— MYRA COHN LIVINGSTON

and a slice of moon

It is a slice of moon, they cry,
A slice of slivered moon in a green sky.

Deep within; (perhaps); it is a fish, a bird, a tree,
Or all the pictures you would make it be.

from Abstract Picture: At the Museum
(first and last stanzas)
— MYRA COHN LIVINGSTON

Hi-Rise

When I move into you,
I'll go straight to the roof
And rub noses with the sky.

— BOBBI KATZ

TOWN
and people

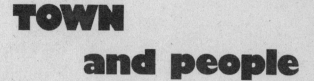

Trip: San Francisco

I went to San Francisco.
I saw the bridges high
Spun across the water
Like cobwebs in the sky.

— LANGSTON HUGHES

Faces

Coming toward me, faces.
Faces going away.
Worry-worry faces.
Hurry-hurry faces.
Shut-you-out,
closed-down,
downtown faces.

Other faces going places —
nice-inside,
crinkly-eyed,
open, sunny,
hello-honey faces.

And sometimes, too,
the wish-I-knew-you faces.

— MARCI RIDLON

2

City Street

A blue-middied girl
stepped on a line,
broke a dish,
lost a wish.

A boy of nine
shied a ball
(and caught it first bounce
off the wall).

A lady with red hair
led a terrier
with tiny steps,
then carried him over a puddle
with care.

Reading newspapers, side by side,
turning pages, pale-eyed —
a bunch of old men.

Who are they all?
Who *are* they all
that I will never see again?

— FELICE HOLMAN

Bam, Bam, Bam

Pickaxes, pickaxes swinging today,
Plaster clouds flying every which way.

Workmen are covered with white dust like snow,
Oh, come see the great demolition show!

Slam, slam, slam,
Goes the steel wrecking-ball;
Bam, bam, bam
Against a stone wall.

It's raining bricks and wood
In my neighborhood.
Down go the houses,
Down go the stores,
Up goes a building
With forty-seven floors.

Crash goes a chimney,
Pow goes a hall,
Zowie goes a doorway,
Zam goes a wall.

Slam, slam, slam,
Goes the steel wrecking-ball;
Bam, bam, bam,
Changing it all.

— EVE MERRIAM

Catching Quiet

It's hard to catch quiet
In the city.
You have to be quick.
It isn't around long.
You might find it
after the roar of a truck,
before a jet flies by.
You might find it
after the horns stop honking,
before the sirens start.
You might find it
after the ice cream man's bell,
before your friends call you
to play.
But when you find it,
stick it in your heart fast.
Keep it there.
It's a bit of the sky.

— MARCI RIDLON

The 1st*

What I remember about that day
is boxes stacked across the walk
and couch springs curling through the air
and drawers and tables balanced on the curb
and us, hollering,
leaping up and around
happy to have a playground;

nothing about the emptied rooms
nothing about the emptied family

— LUCILLE CLIFTON

* First of the month, when the rent was due, and this
family had to get out of their house.

Stickball

The broomstick bat
Is good.
You've got to be fast,
You've got to dodge.
Stickball's a tough game
In the city.
The ball ricochets
From fender to hood
To stoop—you've got it!
You've got to be fast,
You've got to dodge
In the city.

—Virginia Schonborg

Growing: For Louis

It's tough being short.

    Of course your father tells you not to worry,
    But everyone else is giant, and you're just the way
      you were.
    And this stupid guy says, "Hey, shorty, where'd you
      get the long pants?"
    Or some smart beanpole asks how it feels to be so
      close to the ants?
    And the school nurse says to tell her again how tall
      you are, when you've already told her.
    Oh, my mother says there's really no hurry
    And I'll grow soon enough.

But it's tough being short.

(I wonder if Napoleon got the same old stuff?)

                     — MYRA COHN LIVINGSTON

How I Got To Be a Princess

Yesterday my friend said,
"You look just like a princess."
I could not believe him.
Was he talking to someone else?
I looked behind me
  and
in front of me.
I looked under the bed
  and
on top of the closet.
No one else was there.
Again my friend said,
"You look just like a princess."
He really said it to ME!
I felt all twinkling inside.
That's how I got to be a princess.

— BOBBI KATZ

Passing By the Junkyard

Heaps of headlights
   stare
   at me.

Radiators, wheels
   and
   fan-belts
   smile.

And a thousand
   more parts —
   rusty and new,

Seem to say
   they'd all like
   to go
   on a
   car-ride
   again.

      —CHARLES J. EGITA

My Heavy Chevy

It's green, cool,
It's fast, new,
But it eats up the gas.
I put headers on it,
I jacked it up,
I put chrome stags on it.
It's got hood pins.
It's got a hood scoop,
And it's a 454SS under the hood.

My car—Wild!

—DALLAS BELGARDE

Superzero

Everyone's got
a superhero:

Super
Spider
Plastic
Bat

Man,
my hero's comic book
went out of business.

Take a look
on any rack:
my superhero
got the sack.

My hero failed
to make a mint —
batted zero:
out of print.

— JOHN GOLDTHWAITE

Teevee

In the house
of Mr. and Mrs. Spouse
he and she
would watch teevee
and never a word
between them spoken
until the day
the set was broken.

Then "How do you do?"
said he to she.
"I don't believe
that we've met yet.
Spouse is my name.
What's yours?" he asked.

"Why, mine's the same!"
said she to he,
"Do you suppose that we could be — ?"

But the set came suddenly right about,
and so they never did find out.

— EVE MERRIAM

K

When Kate and Karen
Have their battles,
Katherine tattles.

Why Kay and Katherine
Have a spat,
Kate tells that.

When Katherine and Kate
Their tempers lose,
Kay spreads the news.

But Karen gets
The greatest glory.
She turns a friendly fight
Into a full-length story,
And makes it gory.

— LELAND B. JACOBS

On Mother's Day

On Mother's Day we got up first
so full of plans we almost burst.

We started breakfast right away
as our surprise for Mother's Day.

We picked some flowers, then hurried back
to make the coffee—rather black.

We wrapped our gifts and wrote a card
and boiled the eggs—a little hard.

And then we sang a serenade,
which burned the toast, I am afraid.

But Mother said, amidst our cheers,
"Oh, what a big surprise, my dears,
I've not had such a treat in years."
And she was smiling to her ears!

—AILEEN FISHER

Gah'-Chac-Ah

Grandmother, aged in beauty,
Hands wrinkled and soft,
I knew no other so kind.

— CECIL E. JOHNSON, JR.

I was so lonesome
I felt so alone
Watching people across the room and thinking that
they were talking about me.

— JOAN BERG VICTOR

Walking in the Fog

Out in the fog, out in the fog
All gray and misty white,
I hear some muffled scraps of sound,
But no one is in sight.

Only a voice, only a step.
I strain my eyes to see.
Then suddenly, suddenly from the fog
My friend steps out at me.

— MARGARET HILLERT

Soup

I saw a famous man eating soup.
I say he was lifting a fat broth
Into his mouth with a spoon.
His name was in the newspapers that day
Spelled out in tall black headlines
And thousands of people were talking about him.

        When I saw him,
He sat bending his head over a plate
Putting soup in his mouth with a spoon.

—CARL SANDBURG

The Story-Teller

He talked, and as he talked
Wallpaper came alive;
Suddenly ghosts walked,
And four doors were five;

Calendars ran backward,
And maps had mouths;
Ships went tackward
In a great drowse;

Trains climbed trees,
And soon dripped down
Like honey of bees
On the cold brick town.

He had wakened a worm
In the world's brain,
And nothing stood firm
Until day again.

— MARK VAN DOREN

Old Jake Sutter

Old Jake Sutter has a cabin-hut,
Beneath some willows where the river bends.
His beard is longer than I don't know what,
And woodland creatures are his only friends.
He lives on butternuts and fish and such.
His clothes are faded and are mostly tatters:
But old Jake Sutter doesn't worry much.
He's fed and covered, which is all that matters.

Old Jake Sutter has an outdoor chair,
(A car-seat borrowed from the village dump)
And summer evenings he relaxes there
And talks to sparrows on a nearby stump,
While coons and rabbits or a passing skunk
Serenely amble through his open door
To sniff the stuffing on his sagging bunk
Or knock his frying-pan upon the floor.

— KAYE STARBIRD

21

OUTDOORS
with the animals

A Mountain View

Sunset.
Sierra Nevada:
snow on the soft blue range.

Sky, keep your glittering
moon awhile—
don't let the mountains change.

— ROSE BURGUNDER

Sound of Water

The sound of water is:
Rain,
Lap,
Fold,
Slap,
Gurgle,
Splash,
Churn,
Crash,
Murmur,
Pour,
Ripple,
Roar,
Plunge,
Drip,
Spout,
Skip,
Sprinkle,
Flow,
Ice,
Snow.

— MARY O'NEILL

Stream

Trickling . . .
like a tear
    on some lonely face.

Rain

Falling on me
Like moist petals
    of a rose.

— DARLENE PARISIEN

Haiku

Limbs leap to the sky
Leaves listening in the sun.
A forest—beautiful.

— KEVIN MAAS

All These I Hear

All these I hear:
Whiskers and wings
And other whispering things.
Soft fur and golden eyes
And quiet paws.
Smooth swishing tails,
Transparent fins,
Red feathery gills,
And gleaming rainbow scales.
Fernlike antennae,
Dreamlike velvet wings
With peacock eyes.
Soft dappled flanks,
Wet noses, tapered ears,
The shape of shells.
Small, flashing, feathered emeralds
Fire-flecked.
Soft down, smooth eggs,
And stillness balanced
On long slender legs.

Feathers and fur and fins
And other things
Fill my heart
With their soft whisperings.

— DAHLOV IPCAR

25

The Flying Squirrel

A flying squirrel is the strangest thing!
He hasn't a feather. He hasn't a wing.
Yet through the air he skims and scoots.
He doesn't fly. He parachutes.

— ROWENA BENNETT

Owls Aren't So Smart

That stuff about owls —
Being wise and all that —
If they're really so smart,
Well, how come a bat
Can fly so much better,
Or an eagle fly higher,
Or a hawk can dive faster,
And a crow's so much slyer?
How come a smart owl
Can't soar like a tern?
If owls are so smart,
Why don't they just learn?

— RICHARD SHAW

Encounter

We both stood
heart-stopping
still,

I
in the doorway
the deer
near
the old apple tree,

he
muscle wary
straining
to hear

I
holding breath
to say
do not fear.

In the silence
between us
my thought said
Stay!

Did it snap
like
a twig?
He rose on a curve
and fled.

— LILIAN MOORE

One day
A horse ran fast
He ran so fast that wind,
Sunlight, and all the blue of day
Flew gone!

—WILFORD HORNE, JR.

The Runaway

Once when the snow of the year was beginning to fall,
We stopped by a mountain pasture to say, "Whose colt?"
A little Morgan had one forefoot on the wall,
The other curled at his breast. He dipped his head
And snorted at us. And then he had to bolt.
We heard the miniature thunder where he fled,
And we saw him, or thought we saw him, dim and gray,
Like a shadow against the curtain of falling flakes.
"I think the little fellow's afraid of the snow.
He isn't winter-broken. It isn't play
With the little fellow at all. He's running away.

I doubt if even his mother could tell him, 'Sakes,
It's only weather.' He'd think she didn't know!
Where is his mother? He can't be out alone."
And now he comes again with clatter of stone,
And mounts the wall again with whited eyes
And all his tail that isn't hair up straight.
He shudders his coat as if to throw off flies.
"Whoever it is that leaves him out so late,
When other creatures have gone to stall and bin,
Ought to be told to come and take him in."

— ROBERT FROST

Squirrel

The squirrel in the hickory tree's a
nervous fellow,
all quiver and scurry.
See him

hurl himself upon
a limb
worry a nut
pack his cheeks
race
downtree
to a secret place and
hurry
back
in furry frenzy.

There's something he knows
that makes him
go,
this soft slow
mellow
autumn day.

It has to do with
hunger
in the snow.

— LILIAN MOORE

The Black Snake

Black snake! Black snake!
Curling on the ground,
Rolled like a rubber tire,
Ribbed and round.
Black snake! Black snake!
Looped in a tree,
Limp as a licorice whip
Flung free.
Black snake! Black snake!
Curving down the lawn,
Glides like a wave
With its silver gone.
Black snake! Black snake!
Come and live with me!
I'll feed you and I'll pet you
And then I'll set you free!

— PATRICIA HUBBELL

Tracks in the Snow

I found some tracks in the snow near the hedge
And followed them carefully down to the edge
Of the garden place and on to the spot
Where the bushes grow at the end of our lot.
Around the garage to the gate and through,
The little tracks went and I went, too,
Down the sidewalk and under the tree
Where the swing and the sandbox used to be.
And just when I was beginning to wonder,
There was my cat with her feet tucked under.

— MARGARET HILLERT

from **Puppy**

We bought our puppy
   A brand new bed
But he likes sleeping
   On mine instead.

   —LEE BENNETT HOPKINS

The Kitten

The trouble with a kitten is
THAT
Eventually it becomes a
CAT.

    —OGDEN NASH

An Introduction to Dogs

The dog is man's best friend.
He has a tail on one end.
Up in front he has teeth.
And four legs underneath.

Dogs like to bark.
They like it best after dark.
They not only frighten prowlers away
But also hold the sandman at bay.

A dog that is indoors
To be let out implores.
You let him out and what then?
He wants back in again.

Dogs display reluctance and wrath
If you try to give them a bath.
They bury bones in hideaways
And half the time they trot sideaways.

They cheer up people who are frowning,
And rescue people who are drowning,
They also track mud on beds,
And chew people's clothes to shreds.

Dogs in the country have fun.
They run and run and run.
But in the city this species
Is dragged around on leashes.

Dogs are upright as a steeple
And much more loyal than people.
Well people may be reprehensibler
But that's probably because they are sensibler.

—OGDEN NASH

About Feet

The centipede is not complete
Unless he has one hundred feet.
Spiders must have eight for speed,
And six is what all insects need.
Other creatures by the score
Cannot do with less than four.
But two are quite enough, you know,
To take me where I want to go.

— MARGARET HILLERT

The Ant Village

Somebody up in the rocky pasture
   Heaved the stone over.
Here are the cells and a network of furrows
   In the roots of the clover.

Hundreds of eggs lie fitted in patterns,
   Waxy and yellow.
Hundreds of ants are racing and struggling.
   One little fellow

Shoulders an egg as big as his body,
   Ready for hatching.
Darkness is best, so everyone's rushing,
   Hastily snatching

Egg after egg to the lowest tunnels.
   And suddenly, where
Confusion had been, there now is nothing.
   Ants gone. Cells bare.

     — MARION EDEY AND DOROTHY GRIDER

THE SEASONS
and their sports

Early Spring in the Blackberry Patch

No sign of life above ground yet,

But down below the roots are waking,

Stretching down down down

Green time is coming.

Soon.

—ROBERT FROMAN

When the
Plants begin to
Grow, the grass turns dark green
And the birds begin to sing, it
Is spring.

— VANESSA FRASER

Pony Language

I am in the country in the springtime.
The birds are around me.
My pony comes to me.
He speaks his crazy language.
Only I can understand him.
He asks me to repeat every word he says.
And I do.

— KOOKIE JENKINS

Marbles

Immies.
Purees.
Agates.
Shooters.
In a circle.
In a row.
Immies.
Purees.
Agates.
Shooters.
Knock one out
or down a hole.
Immies.
Purees.
Agates.
Shooters.
If I win,
I keep them all.

— KATHLEEN FRASER

Cinquain

Baseball
Running, sliding
The batter smacks the ball.
It's soaring over the fence; gone!
Home run!

— THERESE LABLANC

Associations

Home to me is not a house
Filled with family faces;
Home is where I slide in free
By rounding all the bases.

A tie to me is not
Clothing like a hat;
It means the game is even up
And I wish I were at bat.

— EVE MERRIAM

Hot Enough to See

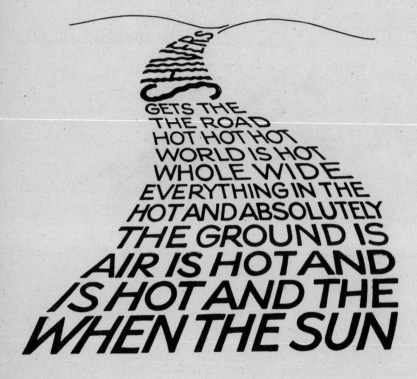

SHIMMERS
GETS THE
THE ROAD
HOT HOT HOT
WORLD IS HOT
WHOLE WIDE
EVERYTHING IN THE
HOT AND ABSOLUTELY
THE GROUND IS
AIR IS HOT AND
IS HOT AND THE
WHEN THE SUN

—ROBERT FROMAN

Thunder!
Noisy, wonder.
Lightning, shattering loud.
The clouds bursting, children
   frightened
Oh, Thor!

— PHILLIP ARENSTEIN

Enchanted Sky

Rose over silver,
Silver over blue.
Golden fountains splashed with green,
And darkness showing through.
Bits of colored stardust
That drift and slowly fade.
What a brief enchanted sky
The fireworks have made!

— MARGARET HILLERT

Ice cream
Is cold, soft, sweet -
So delightful and cool.
It comes in good flavors, too. But . . .
It drips!

—LYNN MEAD

Tomato Time

On a summer vine, and low,
The fat tomatoes burst and grow;

A green, a pink, a yellow head
Will soon be warm and shiny red;

And on a morning, hot with sun,
I'll find and pick a ripened one.

Warm juice and seeds beneath the skin
I'll shut my eyes when I bite in.

—MYRA COHN LIVINGSTON

Day Moon

See,
high in the
blue sea of space
the moon,
a thin golden shell
drifting
faint and far
in the
afternoon.

— DEBRA THURR

Lying in the sun
In midsummer
Looking at a blue sheet
Of happiness.
Only a breath of wind
To spoil it.

— IAN JOHNSON

Driving to the Beach

On the road
smell fumes and tar
through the windows
of the car.

But at the beach
smell suntan lotion
and wind
     and sun
        and ocean!

    — JOANNA COLE

Beach

Close in, near to the sand
Waves come, white and rolling.

Farther out, they turn green
With kelp snaking around the top.

But way beyond, when you squint, you can see
Hundreds of yellow sunshine spitballs.

— MYRA COHN LIVINGSTON

August Weather

Dead heat and windless air,
  And silence over all;
Never a leaf astir,
  But the ripe apples fall;
Plums are purple red,
  Pears amber and brown;
Thud! in the garden-bed!
  Ripe apples fall down.

Air like a cider press
  With the bruised apples' scent;
Low whistles express
  Some sleepy bird's content;
Still world and windless sky,
  A mist of heat o'er all;
Peace like a lullaby,
  And the ripe apples fall.

— KATHARINE TYNAN

50

A leaf crashes gently to the ground
A cricket lands lightly on it
And tunes itself for a song.

— JENNIFER HODGMAN

from **Autumn**

Come! let us draw the curtains,
   heap up the fire and sit
hunched by the flame together,
   and make a friend of it.

Listen! the wind is rising,
   and the air is wild with leaves,
we have had our summer evenings:
   now for October eves!

— HUMBERT WOLFE

Eight Witches

Eight witches rode the midnight sky.
One wailed low, and one wailed high,
Another croaked, another sighed
Throughout the eerie midnight ride.

One witch's voice was cackly toned,
Another shrieked, another moaned.
The eighth, much younger than the rest,
Made a scary sound the best—
A scream to make the blood run blue:
Yoooo—
    Yoooo—
        Yoooo—
            Yoooo—

—B. J. LEE

from **Deserted**

The old house leans upon a tree
   Like some old man upon a staff:
The night wind in its ancient porch
   Sounds like a hollow laugh.

The dark is full of whispers. Now
   A fox-hound howls: and through the night,
Like some old ghost from out its grave,
   The moon comes misty white.

         — MADISON CAWEIN

The cemetery stones are walking
in the final shadows of the light,
white beneath the village stars,
tilting away to night.

         — GEORGE MENDOZA

A Football Game

It's the might, it's the fight
Of two teams who won't give in —
It's the roar of the crowd
And the "Go, fight, win!"

It's the bands, it's the stands,
It's the color everywhere.
It's the whiff, it's the sniff
Of the popcorn on the air.

It's a thrill, it's a chill,
It's a cheer and then a sigh;
It's that deep, breathless hush
When the ball soars high.

Yes, it's more than a score,
Or a desperate grasp at fame;
Fun is King, win or lose —
That's a football game.

—ALICE VAN ECK

Kickoff

In the beginning was the

Kickoff.
The ball flew
spiralling true
into the end zone
where it was snagged,
neatly hugged
by a swivel-hipped back
who ran up the field
and was smeared.

The game has begun.
The game has been won.
The game goes on.
Long live the game.
Gather and lock
tackle and block
move, move,
around the arena
and always the beautiful
trajectories.

— LILLIAN MORRISON

Wind and Silver

Greatly shining,
The Autumn moon floats in the thin sky;
And the fish-ponds shake their backs and flash their
   dragon scales
As she passes over them.

— AMY LOWELL

Winter Season

Deep in the mountains we have no calendar
To tell us when the seasons change.
Flowers bloom — we guess that it is spring;
Leaves fall, so it is autumn.

And when children hunt for warm clothes,
We know it must be winter!

—Anonymous

Snowflakes

Snowflakes
Whirling
Twirling
Swirling

Gliding up
Falling down
Softly circling
To the ground.

— DEBBIE HASTINGS

The First Christmas

There wasn't any Christmas tree,
Or decorations hung up high.
There wasn't the bother of giving cards
Or any presents to buy.

There weren't any lights to hang
Or shopping to be done.
They wasn't any Santa Claus;
Just a mother and her son.

— RHONDA WHEWELL

Winter

Winter doesn't have picnics
under the bright green leaves,

But winter has daggers of icicles
that dangle from the eaves.

Winter doesn't have swimming,
or camping, or balls to bat,

But winter has Christmas, and nothing,
nothing is better than that.

— AILEEN FISHER

Skating

We glitter and fly
Beneath the sky
And lean against the gale.

Our feet wear blades
Of diamond dust;
We etch a frosty trail.

The brittle pond
Is ringed with snow,
The pines are brushed with black.

Around we skim,
Around the rim,
Around the rim, and back.

— Barbara Juster Esbensen

JUST FOR FUN

Winter Remedy

It seems to me it would be fair,
If three gloves came in every pair.
Then on cold days I wouldn't mind,
If there was one I couldn't find!

— BOBBI KATZ

I eat my peas with honey,
I've done it all my life,
It makes the peas taste funny,
But it keeps them on my knife.

— ANONYMOUS

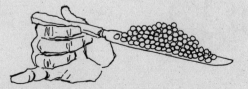

The Porcupine

Rebecca Jane,
a friend of mine,
went out to pat
a porcupine.

She very shortly
came back in,
disgusted with
the porcupin.

"One never, ever
should," said Jane,
"go out and pat
a porcupain!"

—N. M. BODECKER

Up State

Up state
and down state,
a smart alligator
ran for the office
of state legislator.
He said: "If elected,
true to my nature,
I'll put teeth in your laws
—and your state legislature."

from Up and Down (fourth stanza)
    —N. M. BODECKER

Tongue Twisters

You've no need to light a night light
On a light night like tonight,
For a night light's light's a slight light,
And tonight's a night that's light.
When a night's light, like tonight's light,
It is really not quite right
To light night lights with their slight lights
On a light night like tonight.

—ANONYMOUS

Noses

I suppose that a nose
Is as long as it grows,
And that's why the elephant's
Touches his toes.

—ROWENA BENNETT

Limericks

Arthur

There was an old man of Calcutta,
Who coated his tonsils with butta,
Thus converting his snore
From a thunderous roar
To a soft, oleaginous mutta.

— OGDEN NASH

Edouard

A bugler named Dougal MacDougal
Found ingenious ways to be frugal.
He learned how to sneeze
In various keys,
Thus saving the price of a bugle.

— OGDEN NASH

The Lamb

Little gamboling lamb,
Do you know where you am?
In a patch of mint.
I'll give you a hint:
Scram,
Lamb!

—OGDEN NASH

The Termite

Some primal termite knocked on wood
And tasted it and found it good,
And that is why your Aunt May
Fell through the parlor floor today.

—OGDEN NASH

Some lollipops last a long long time. You lick and you lick and you lick and you keep on licking and licking until all you have left to lick is the empty lollipop stick.

—RUTH BELOV GROSS

A Thought

Birthdays and Christmas
Would both be better
If no one expected
A thank-you letter.

— Marchette Chute

If you ever
Take a bath,
Even though you don't expect to,
Simply turn the water off
And you'll find it won't affect you.

— Arnold Spilka

Mean Song

Snickles and podes,
Ribble and grodes:
That's what I wish you.

A nox in the groot,
A root in the stoot
And a gock in the forbeshaw, too.

Keep out of sight
For fear that I might
Glom you a gravely snave.

Don't show your face
Around any place
Or you'll get one flack snack in the bave.

— EVE MERRIAM

Coney Island

Foto you,
Foto me,
Pull the curtains,
Count to three.

(Argle, gargle,
Flap and roll;
Horrible faces
Are good for the soul.

Argle,
Gargle . . .)

Click
Click
Paid:

25¢
To the Penny Arcade.

— JOHN GOLDTHWAITE

THOUGHTS ABOUT THIS AND THAT

Spectacular

Listen,
a bird is singing.
Look,
up there!
He's on the rooftop
clinging
to the TV aerial,
singing
on prime time —
and no sponsor!

— LILIAN MOORE

from **Univac to Univac**

(sotto voce)

Now that he's left the room,
Let me ask you something, as computer to computer.
That fellow who just closed the door behind him—
The servant who feeds us cards and paper tape—
Have you ever taken a good look at him and his kind?

—LOUIS B. SALOMON

Coca-Cola Sunset

Through the arch of the bridge
the Coca-Cola sign
lights red neon
in the muddy sky —
a hemisphere
in the gray-smoked sky
a guzzling red
in the wet dusk sky
on the wet road bed
on the slimy shore —
a setting sun
in the arch of the bridge.

— FELICE HOLMAN

Mistake

Once it was a farm.
    "Here at Acme we manufacture plastics,
    everything from wire to elastics."

I lived here once — grew up here, in fact.
    "Last year we began to expand;
    we laid out eighty thousand for this land."

I milked the cows, planted, dreamed.
    "The factory you are about to enter
    is an ultra-modern manufacturing center."

My father owned it, and his father before him.
  "Yes, sir. We're going to create new products here;
  plastic hats, flowers, and cans for beer."

When he died I decided to sell.
That money looked awfully good.
But now,
Seeing this—this factory,
I miss that farm.

— MICHAEL MAGER

Three Skies

Three skies
Above our world —

Grey sky when clouds are high.

Break through the clouds
And it's blue where the planes fly.

Break through the blue on a rocket flight
And the skies are black, day and night.

Break through the black —
   Who knows
   To what fourth sky,
   On what flight?

               — CLAUDIA LEWIS

If I Could Be an Astronaut

If I could be an astronaut,
I would like to go
To a planet full of colors
Where flowers grow in snow.
I wouldn't go to Venus.
I wouldn't go to Mars.
I'd find a kind of special place
Somewhere among the stars.
A place where fish have feathers,
A place where trees can talk,
That's where I'll land my spaceship
And take a weightless walk.

— BOBBI KATZ

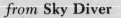

from **Sky Diver**

Grotesque, jumping out
like a clothed frog, helmet and glasses,
arms and legs wading the sky,
feet flapping before the cloth flower opens;
then suspended, poised,
an exclamation point upside-down,
and going down, swaying over corn and creeks
and highways scribbled
over the bones of fish and eagles.

— ADRIEN STOUTENBERG

Flight

You know the sitting on the train not-knowing feeling
As to which is moving, you or the station?
You can do it with the whole earth if you know how.
Give up? Stand by night in a silent snowfall, perhaps
   under a street lamp.
If the flakes are large and falling steadily and the wind
   has gone to bed
And you look straight up, eventually it is the flakes that
   are motionless, white blobs of paint on a canvas,
And you and the whole earth (which is magnetized to
   your feet bottoms) are floating softly, airily up.

The ride lasts only a few seconds because
Your "senses" intrude.
But it's lovely while it lasts. If you can take it
   come back and tell me.
I've almost forgotten.

—STEVE ALLEN

You Can Go Now

You can go now yes go now. Go east or west, go north or
    south, you can go now. Or you can go up or go down now.
    And after these there is no place to go. If you say no
    to all of them then you stay here. You don't go. You
    are fixed and put. And from here if you choose you send
    up rockets, you let down buckets. Here then for you
    is the centre of things.

—CARL SANDBURG

Ignore dull days; forget the showers;
Keep count of only shining hours.

—FOUND ON A GERMAN SUNDIAL

A dream
   and a star
shine best
   from afar!

— JOAN WALSH ANGLUND

What Is Once Loved

What is once loved
You will find
Is always yours
From that day.
Take it home
In your mind
And nothing ever
Can take it away.

— ELIZABETH COATSWORTH

The Secret Sits

We dance round in a ring and suppose,
But the Secret sits in the middle and knows.

— ROBERT FROST

When time was a boy
I brought the summer earth humming
to my head
and looked at a mountain
through a blade of grass.
The blade of grass, I saw, was taller than the
mountain.
The blade of grass, I dreamed, was taller than
the world.
So I picked it and stuffed it in my pocket,
a mountain and a world.

                    —GEORGE MENDOZA

Index of Titles and Authors

84

Index of First Lines